ABOUT DR. KIMBERLY:

Dr. Kimberly M. Martin is a clinical psychologist who is passionate about social justice, increasing access to mental health care, and decreasing the stigma associated with mental health. Trained in Individual Adlerian Psychology, Dr. Kimberly also combines Buddhist philosophy, mediation, yoga, and mind-body practices in her work with individuals and the community.   In addition to individual services, Dr. Kimberly provides services to the community through Tea and Therapy™ workshops, podcasts, and collaborations.

DISCLAIMER

This journal was written for personal use, education, and entertainment purposes. Information presented here is not a substitute for psychology/medical advice. Any person with a condition requiring psychological or psychiatric attention should consult a qualified psychologist or suitable mental health practitioner.

DEDICATION

This journal is the result of several decades of steeped tea. I dedicate this book to my ancestors for all their work, perseverance, and love. To all my teachers who provided me with encouragement and guidance. To those who sat in my office chair and continually showed me the power of hope.

A special thank you to Dr. Charolette Ray, who sat with me for many years over cups of tea.

SIPS OF TEA

Sips of tea is a seven-week self-exploration journal designed to help you deepen your understanding of self, identify and examine the underlying root causes of difficulties and personal concerns. The author developed questions in this journal based on lived and professional experiences. Teachings in Buddhism, meditation, yoga, mind and bodywork, Adlerian, and general psychology influenced to queries in this journal

The history of Sakyamuni Buddha, who obtained enlightenment after seven weeks of meditation, motivated the journal's seven-week format. The first six days of the week contain space for thorough responses to three writing prompts or the creation of tables/schedules. The seventh day of the week allows for a brief reflection. Should a question appear repetitive, take a deep breath, take a sip of tea, and dive deeper.

This workbook may be completed alone, with a group, or share your insights with your psychologist or other mental health professional. Each chapter begins with a summary of tea to add to the ritual of healing and indulge your senses while you savor your meditative and reflective moments

WHY TEA?

Tea is an element used for centuries in mental and physical health. The sequence of preparing, serving, and sipping tea offers steps necessary for ritual and healing. Tea and therapy are coping and stress management skills that promote healing. Two components in tea, caffeine, and L-Theanine are known to reduce stress and create alertness without overstimulating the nervous system. Tea clears the mind and lifts spirits. The selection of tea and therapy depends on the mood and nature of the ailment.

MAKING A CUP OF TEA*

1. Heat the water
   a. Put fresh water into a kettle
   b. Heat the water according to the type of tea
      i. 208°F/98°C for Black tea
      ii. 195°F/90°C for Oolong tea
      iii. 175°F/80°C for Green tea
      iv. 165°F/80°C for White tea
      v. 208°F/98°C for Herbal tea
   c. Preheat the teapot or cup by pouring in a small amount of water.
2. Steep the tea
   a. Place the tea leaves (or bags) into the teapot or cup (add a tea ball or strainer if using tea leaves)
   b. Pour hot water over the tea
   c. Steep the tea based on the type of tea (the longer you steep the tea, the stronger the flavor)
      i. 5 minutes for Black tea
      ii. 2-3 minutes for Oolong tea
      iii. 2-4 minutes for Green Tea
      iv. 2-3 minutes for white tea
      v. 4-5 minutes for Herbal tea
   d. Strain the tea leaves or remove the teabag
3. Drink the tea
   a. Enjoy your cup of tea on its own to enjoy the flavors.
   b. Milk, sweetener, and lemon may be added to taste.

* (*Steeping temperature and times may vary based on the tea and taste preference*)

TEA: TEACH EMPOWER ADVOCATE!

THE BEGINNING PREPARATIONS

You will engage in significant work during the next seven weeks. Before you make changes, you will need to perform an accurate assessment, set realistic and attainable goals, and determine the consequences of change. This first week allows a gentle exploration into the study of self and tools needed for your journey.

The foundation for the work ahead begins with this first week. This week, you will examine your intentions for beginning this journal and your readiness level for a change.

DAY 1
What were your intentions in purchasing this journal?

_____

_____

_____

_____

_____

_____

_____

_____

_____

_____

_____

_____

_____

_____

_____

_____

_____

_____

_____

_____

_____

_____

_____

_____

_____

DAY 1
What do you hope to discover about yourself?

_____

_____

_____

_____

_____

_____

_____

_____

_____

_____

_____

_____

_____

_____

_____

_____

_____

_____

_____

_____

_____

_____

_____

DAY 1
What do you hope you will have accomplished after forty-nine days of journaling?

_____

_____

_____

_____

_____

_____

_____

_____

_____

_____

_____

_____

_____

_____

_____

_____

_____

_____

_____

_____

_____

_____

_____

_____

DAY 2

Describe the current situations in your life: (Areas to consider are personal relationships, mental health, physical health, emotions, finances, living arrangements)

_____

_____

_____

_____

_____

_____

_____

_____

_____

_____

_____

_____

_____

_____

_____

_____

_____

_____

_____

_____

_____

_____

_____

_____

DAY 2
What would you like to change?

_____

_____

_____

_____

_____

_____

_____

_____

_____

_____

_____

_____

_____

_____

_____

_____

_____

_____

_____

_____

_____

_____

_____

DAY 2
What will your life look like once the changes happen?

_____

_____

_____

_____

_____

_____

_____

_____

_____

_____

_____

_____

_____

_____

_____

_____

_____

_____

_____

_____

_____

_____

DAY 3

The responses from today will examine the degree of control you have regarding changes in your life.
Based on your answers from Day 2:

What outside factors hinder a change in your life?

_____

_____

_____

_____

_____

_____

_____

_____

_____

_____

_____

_____

_____

_____

_____

_____

_____

_____

_____

_____

_____

_____

DAY 3
What situations are within your power to make a change?

DAY 3
What situations must you accept?

_____

_____

_____

_____

_____

_____

_____

_____

_____

_____

_____

_____

_____

_____

_____

_____

_____

_____

_____

_____

_____

_____

_____

_____

_____

DAY 4

Change can seem like a storm, with unpredictable highs and lows. As we encounter life, it is essential to identify our stage of the storm and anchors.
As you think of your life and life changes, where are you?

Describe the beginning, middle, or end of the storm.

_____

_____

_____

_____

_____

_____

_____

_____

_____

_____

_____

_____

_____

_____

_____

_____

_____

_____

_____

_____

_____

DAY 4

What's happening now? Are you buckling in, riding it out, or accessing the aftermath and moving forward?

_____

_____

_____

_____

_____

_____

_____

_____

_____

_____

_____

_____

_____

_____

_____

_____

_____

_____

_____

_____

_____

_____

_____

DAY 4
Describe your anchor during this time of change.

_____

_____

_____

_____

_____

_____

_____

_____

_____

_____

_____

_____

_____

_____

_____

_____

_____

_____

_____

_____

_____

_____

_____

_____

_____

DAY 5

There are five primary stages of change: Precontemplation (nothing needs to change), Contemplation (something needs to change), action (making the change), Relapse (going back), and maintenance (making the new changes a part of your life).

What is your current level of change?

_____

_____

_____

_____

_____

_____

_____

_____

_____

_____

_____

_____

_____

_____

_____

_____

_____

_____

_____

_____

_____

DAY 5
What is your next level of change, and what needs to happen to reach the next level?

DAY 5
How long do you think it will take to see the change in your life?

_____
_____
_____
_____
_____
_____
_____
_____
_____
_____
_____
_____
_____
_____
_____
_____
_____
_____
_____
_____
_____
_____
_____
_____
_____
_____
_____

DAY 6

While the focus of change may be on one situation or behavior, connection dictates that one change impacts another.

How might your change impact other areas in your life?

_____

_____

_____

_____

_____

_____

_____

_____

_____

_____

_____

_____

_____

_____

_____

_____

_____

_____

_____

_____

_____

DAY 6
What might you gain as a result of this change?

DAY 6
How are you prepared for the results of your actions?

DAY 7
Take the space today and reflect on your responses from this week. Write about your observations:

_____

_____

_____

_____

_____

_____

_____

_____

_____

_____

_____

_____

_____

_____

_____

_____

_____

_____

_____

_____

_____

_____

_____

Are you ready to move forward to week two?

BLACK TEA

Black tea is the most common tea in Europe and North America. Black tea is fully fermented as the tea leaves are rolled and oxidized (the process of browning and flavoring the tea leaves). Black tea is bold and complex and often has higher levels of caffeine than other teas. Best when the water is boiled at 208°F/98°C and steeped 3-5 minutes for full leaves and tea bags. Black tea contains a group of polyphenols with antioxidant properties that may reduce chronic disease risk and improve your overall health. Black tea can aid in lowering blood pressure and preventing heart disease.

There is something in the nature of tea that leads us into a world of quiet contemplation of life – Lin Yutang

MINDFULNESS AND MEDITATION

Last week started the groundwork on identifying the areas and stages of change and the initial work on goal identification. Change can be difficult; you may develop resistance, this resistance may lead to discomfort, and you may want to stop movement in your change process. For change to occur, it's important to have the necessary tools to adjust to change and know when your body and mind are creating resistance. This week will focus on meditation and mindfulness, skills required in creating awareness and processing resistance.

Meditation allows one an opportunity to look at self, a tool of self-exploration, and for some, a chance to slow down, and yes, maybe even sit still. This week may be a review of a process that you've already begun or a more in-depth journey/awakening for those familiar with meditation. Before exploring the technique, it's important to remember a few things about meditation. 1. The objective is to observe your thoughts and body sensations. 2. Quieting thoughts is not the primary goal. 3. Connecting with the breath is the essential task. You may perform this exercise with or without music. The preference is to engage in these activities from a seated position.

As you move through journaling this week, begin each session with a minimum of five minutes of breathing, engaging in deep abdominal breaths where the abdominal area rises as you inhale and deflates as you exhale.

DAY 8

Exercise: *The breath is a tool that can assess emotional and physical well-being and serve as a guide for a meditative journey. Allow yourself to spend a minimum of five minutes sitting quietly and focusing on the rise and fall of your abdominal area as you inhale and exhale. Should you become distracted from focusing on your breath, gently return your awareness to your breath.*

What did you notice while focusing on your breath?

_____

_____

_____

_____

_____

_____

_____

_____

_____

_____

_____

_____

_____

_____

_____

_____

_____

_____

_____

DAY 8
What did you notice in your thoughts?

_____

_____

_____

_____

_____

_____

_____

_____

_____

_____

_____

_____

_____

_____

_____

_____

_____

_____

_____

_____

_____

_____

DAY 8

Exercise: The breath is a tool that can assess emotional and physical well-being and serve as a guide for a meditative journey. Allow yourself to spend a minimum of five minutes sitting quietly and focusing on the rise and fall of your abdominal area as you inhale and exhale. Should you become distracted from focusing on your breath, gently return your awareness to your breath.

What did you notice while focusing on your breath?

_____

_____

_____

_____

_____

_____

_____

_____

_____

_____

_____

_____

_____

_____

_____

_____

_____

_____

_____

DAY 8
What did you notice in your thoughts?

_____

_____

_____

_____

_____

_____

_____

_____

_____

_____

_____

_____

_____

_____

_____

_____

_____

_____

_____

_____

_____

_____

_____

DAY 8
What is needed to increase your physical comfort while engaging in meditation?

_____

_____

_____

_____

_____

_____

_____

_____

_____

_____

_____

_____

_____

_____

_____

_____

_____

_____

_____

_____

_____

DAY 9

Before you begin to write today, spend at least five minutes observing your breath. When you are ready, respond to the following questions:

How long were you able to engage in meditation today?

_____

_____

_____

_____

_____

_____

_____

_____

_____

_____

_____

_____

_____

_____

_____

_____

_____

_____

_____

_____

_____

_____

DAY 9
What insights did you obtain during today's practice?

_____

_____

_____

_____

_____

_____

_____

_____

_____

_____

_____

_____

_____

_____

_____

_____

_____

_____

_____

_____

_____

_____

_____

_____

DAY 9

What were other things you noticed during today's practice? (thoughts, emotions, and physical feelings)

_____

_____

_____

_____

_____

_____

_____

_____

_____

_____

_____

_____

_____

_____

_____

_____

_____

_____

_____

_____

_____

Move through your day today as a casual observer, just noticing.

DAY 10

Mindfulness is an act of being aware, an opportunity to be mindful of the senses without judgment. At the end of yesterday's journaling, you were asked to go about your day as an observer, as you reflect upon yesterday and your life...

What are the things that you notice the most in your life?

_____
_____
_____
_____
_____
_____
_____
_____
_____
_____
_____
_____
_____
_____
_____
_____
_____
_____
_____
_____
_____
_____

DAY 10
What are things that may be less noticeable in your life?

_____

_____

_____

_____

_____

_____

_____

_____

_____

_____

_____

_____

_____

_____

_____

_____

_____

_____

_____

_____

_____

_____

_____

DAY 10

What is one thing you want to observe for the remainder of the week? (You may begin with one of your senses or thoughts).

_____

_____

_____

_____

_____

_____

_____

_____

_____

_____

_____

_____

_____

_____

_____

_____

_____

_____

_____

_____

_____

_____

_____

DAY 11

As you focused on mindfulness over the past few days, you may have noticed the ability to engage in mindfulness while being still and while moving. Mindfulness can occur in many everyday activities. Mindful eating may involve noticing the aroma of food before eating, slow chewing, and eating in silence. A simple act of noticing water temperature and the water's feel as it slides over dishes can be a task of mindfulness. Yoga is an example of mindful movement.

Where have you been able to engage in mindfulness?

_____

_____

_____

_____

_____

_____

_____

_____

_____

_____

_____

_____

_____

_____

_____

_____

_____

_____

_____

_____

DAY 11
How do you involve your body in mindful movement?

_____

_____

_____

_____

_____

_____

_____

_____

_____

_____

_____

_____

_____

_____

_____

_____

_____

_____

_____

_____

_____

_____

_____

DAY 11
What do you notice when engaged in activities of mindfulness?

_____

_____

_____

_____

_____

_____

_____

_____

_____

_____

_____

_____

_____

_____

_____

_____

_____

_____

_____

_____

_____

_____

DAY 12

Over the past days, you may have been more aware of your breath. Breath can guide you in managing anxiety and keeping yourself grounded in the present moment when your thoughts take you to the past or future. Thinking about your breathing...

What are the situations in your life when your breath was rapid and shallow?

_____

_____

_____

_____

_____

_____

_____

_____

_____

_____

_____

_____

_____

_____

_____

_____

_____

_____

_____

_____

_____

DAY 12
When is your breath more likely to be calm and steady?

DAY 12
Where and when will you begin to implement conscious breathing into your life?

_____

_____

_____

_____

_____

_____

_____

_____

_____

_____

_____

_____

_____

_____

_____

_____

_____

_____

_____

_____

_____

_____

_____

_____

DAY 13

What have you noticed as you've increased your involvement in mindfulness and breathwork over the past few days?

_____
_____
_____
_____
_____
_____
_____
_____
_____
_____
_____
_____
_____
_____
_____
_____
_____
_____
_____
_____
_____
_____
_____
_____
_____

DAY 13
What were your unexpected observations?

_____

_____

_____

_____

_____

_____

_____

_____

_____

_____

_____

_____

_____

_____

_____

_____

_____

_____

_____

_____

_____

_____

_____

DAY 13
In what ways will you continue to implement mindfulness and meditation in your life?

_____

_____

_____

_____

_____

_____

_____

_____

_____

_____

_____

_____

_____

_____

_____

_____

_____

_____

_____

_____

_____

_____

_____

_____

_____

DAY 13
What were your unexpected observations?

_____

_____

_____

_____

_____

_____

_____

_____

_____

_____

_____

_____

_____

_____

_____

_____

_____

_____

_____

_____

_____

_____

DAY 13

In what ways will you continue to implement mindfulness and meditation in your life?

_____

_____

_____

_____

_____

_____

_____

_____

_____

_____

_____

_____

_____

_____

_____

_____

_____

_____

_____

_____

_____

_____

_____

_____

_____

DAY 13
What were your unexpected observations?

_____

_____

_____

_____

_____

_____

_____

_____

_____

_____

_____

_____

_____

_____

_____

_____

_____

_____

_____

_____

_____

_____

_____

DAY 13
In what ways will you continue to implement mindfulness and meditation in your life?

DAY 14

What are your observations about mindfulness, meditation, and breathwork? What are your reflections on the past two weeks of journaling?

_____

_____

_____

_____

_____

_____

_____

_____

_____

_____

_____

_____

_____

_____

_____

_____

_____

_____

_____

_____

Additional recommended readings: Gunaratana, H. (2002). Mindfulness in plain English. Boston: Wisdom Publications. Hart, W. (1987). The art of living: Vipassana meditation as taught by S.N. Goenka. San Francisco: Harper & Row.

OOLONG TEA

Oolong tea is oxidized in the sunlight and falls between green and black tea regarding flavor and caffeine levels. The caffeine level of Oolong tea increases, the longer the tea is steeped. Oolong may have more of a bitter taste than Black or Green tea.   Best when the water is boiled at 195°F/90°C and for 5-7 minutes for loose leaf and 3-5 minutes for teabags.   Oolong tea can assist in lowering blood pressure and cholesterol and improving sleep. Oolong also stimulates fat burning and helps metabolism rates.

"Tea unleashes the potential which slumbers in the depth of my soul.
-Leo Tolstoy

EARLY RECOLLECTIONS

Now that you've had an opportunity and experience sitting with emotions, and possible discomfort, let's begin the deepening process by examining early influences and identity development. This week you will explore the relationship between early life experiences, core beliefs, and current life experiences. Continue to use deep breathing, meditation, and mindfulness as you continue to reflect upon the prompts this week and throughout the rest of this journal.

DAY 15

Core beliefs are thoughts developed from early experiences. Core beliefs may impact the way you maneuver through life.

Thinking of your earlier experiences, preferably before the age of 5, how would you complete the following sentences (Complete these as if you are your younger self)

I am:

_____

Others are:

_____

The world is:

_____

Therefore, to find a place in the world, I
must:_____

How would you respond to the above statements now?

_____
_____
_____
_____
_____
_____
_____
_____
_____
_____
_____
_____
_____
_____
_____
_____
_____

DAY 15
What are the differences between your past and current views?

DAY 15
Based on your current responses, what views would you like to change?

_____
_____
_____
_____
_____
_____
_____
_____
_____
_____
_____
_____
_____
_____
_____
_____
_____
_____
_____
_____
_____
_____
_____
_____
_____
_____
_____

DAY 15
What are the differences between your past and current views?

DAY 15
Based on your current responses, what views would you like to change?

_____

_____

_____

_____

_____

_____

_____

_____

_____

_____

_____

_____

_____

_____

_____

_____

_____

_____

_____

_____

_____

_____

_____

DAY 16

As you were growing up, what was your role in your family? (examples include: Peacemaker, Parent's helper, to keep the family together, the good kid, the troublemaker).

_____

_____

_____

_____

_____

_____

_____

_____

_____

_____

_____

_____

_____

_____

_____

_____

_____

_____

_____

_____

_____

DAY 16

If you were to use a weather term to describe your upbringing, what would it be? (examples: Sunny, Cloudy, Thunderstorm, Cold)

_____

_____

_____

_____

_____

_____

_____

_____

_____

_____

_____

_____

_____

_____

_____

_____

_____

_____

_____

_____

_____

_____

_____

DAY 16

As you were growing up, what was your role in your family? (examples include: Peacemaker, Parent's helper, to keep the family together, the good kid, the troublemaker).

_____
_____
_____
_____
_____
_____
_____
_____
_____
_____
_____
_____
_____
_____
_____
_____
_____
_____
_____
_____
_____

DAY 16

If you were to use a weather term to describe your upbringing, what would it be? (examples: Sunny, Cloudy, Thunderstorm, Cold)

_____

_____

_____

_____

_____

_____

_____

_____

_____

_____

_____

_____

_____

_____

_____

_____

_____

_____

_____

_____

_____

_____

DAY 16
What did you want or need most as a child?

_____

_____

_____

_____

_____

_____

_____

_____

_____

_____

_____

_____

_____

_____

_____

_____

_____

_____

_____

_____

_____

_____

_____

DAY 17
What have been significant events in your childhood? (Recall 1 or 2 events)

DAY 17
What meaning have you given to these events?

DAY 17
How do these events and the meaning you've given to these events impact you today?

_____

_____

_____

_____

_____

_____

_____

_____

_____

_____

_____

_____

_____

_____

_____

_____

_____

_____

_____

_____

_____

_____

_____

DAY 18

Intersectionality is a term used to describe the various traits/characteristics of an individual. These characteristics include but are not limited to gender, race, ethnicity, sexual orientation, age, occupation, and income level. The relationship between an individual's intersectionality and environment can impact overall physical and mental well-being.

How does the world see/define/label you?

_____

_____

_____

_____

_____

_____

_____

_____

_____

_____

_____

_____

_____

_____

_____

_____

_____

_____

_____

_____

_____

_____

_____

DAY 18

What is true/untrue about this view/definition/label? How does it compare to how you see/define/label yourself?

_____

_____

_____

_____

_____

_____

_____

_____

_____

_____

_____

_____

_____

_____

_____

_____

_____

_____

_____

_____

_____

_____

_____

_____

DAY 18

What is the relationship between your intersectionality and your environment? To what extent do your surroundings foster a feeling of safety, security, and belonging?

_____

_____

_____

_____

_____

_____

_____

_____

_____

_____

_____

_____

_____

_____

_____

_____

_____

_____

_____

_____

_____

_____

_____

DAY 19

Adlerian/Individual Psychology proposes that childhood circumstances, adolescent experiences, and personal perceptions determine how well an individual will maneuver through the adult tasks of relationships with others, love and sex, work, and spirituality.

In which life task are you currently experiencing the most difficulty, or what task requires improvement?

_____

_____

_____

_____

_____

_____

_____

_____

_____

_____

_____

_____

_____

_____

_____

_____

_____

_____

_____

_____

_____

_____

_____

DAY 19
How are difficulties in this life task connected to childhood memories?

DAY 19
What are ways you can begin improving this task?

DAY 20

In what way does your current situation resemble any past experiences/situations?

DAY 20
What previous thoughts, behaviors may have been productive in the past but aren't useful now?

_____

_____

_____

_____

_____

_____

_____

_____

_____

_____

_____

_____

_____

_____

_____

_____

_____

_____

_____

_____

_____

_____

_____

_____

_____

DAY 20
What was helpful in the former situation that may benefit you now?

_____

_____

_____

_____

_____

_____

_____

_____

_____

_____

_____

_____

_____

_____

_____

_____

_____

_____

_____

_____

_____

_____

_____

DAY 21

List the changes you would like to see in your core beliefs at the completion of this workbook.
I am_____, Others are _____, The world is _____, therefore in order
to find a place in the world where I feel safe, secure, and connected I must _____.
Record additional reflections you have for this week.

_____

_____

_____

_____

_____

_____

_____

_____

_____

_____

_____

_____

_____

_____

_____

_____

_____

_____

_____

_____

_____

GREEN TEA

Green tea is a delicate tea that is not fermented but undergoes steaming, roasting, and drying. Best when the water is boiled at 175°F/80°C and steeped 2-4 minutes for loose leaves and 1-3 minutes for teabags. Green tea has less caffeine than black tea and offers a more delicate flavor. Green tea contains an average of 25 mg of caffeine. Green tea contains antioxidants and free radicals, which boost the immune system and assist with metabolism. Green tea may decrease anxiety and improve memory and sleep patterns. If you'd like to detect green tea's subtle flavors, try the beverage without sweetener or milk.

"When I drink tea, I am conscious of peace. The cool breath of heaven rises in my sleeves and blows my cares away." – Lo Tung

MOOD AND EMOTIONS

This week the focus is on exploring mood and the development of coping strategies to identify and manage emotions. Continue to utilize mindfulness, meditation, and breathing techniques, also notice the connections between your moods and earlier experiences in your life. Do your moods and emotions have patterns?

DAY 22

On a scale of 0-5 (0= manageable 5 = unmanageable), rate and describe your emotions (you may pick one or more emotions to focus on today or identify one word to express your emotions).

_____

_____

_____

_____

_____

_____

_____

_____

_____

_____

_____

_____

_____

_____

_____

_____

_____

_____

_____

_____

_____

_____

_____

_____

_____

_____

_____

DAY 22
Thinking of your current concerns, which ones are related to the future
and which ones are related to the past?

_____
_____
_____
_____
_____
_____
_____
_____
_____
_____
_____
_____
_____
_____
_____
_____
_____
_____
_____
_____
_____
_____
_____
_____
_____
_____
_____

DAY 22
As you think of your emotions, what's your biggest source of suffering?
What's giving you the most difficulty?

DAY 23

Many individuals report experiencing the emotion and feeling of anxiety. Anxiety can be related to feelings and thoughts and also manifest as physical sensations. Deep breathing exercises, movement activities, and muscle relaxation manage the physical sensations that accompany anxiety. The following prompts address thoughts that may be associated with anxiety.

Thinking of situations when you experienced anxiety, what have (had) you made up about your future?

_____

_____

_____

_____

_____

_____

_____

_____

_____

_____

_____

_____

_____

_____

_____

_____

_____

_____

_____

_____

_____

_____

DAY 23
In what situations do you feel unprepared?

DAY 23
What's currently unfinished in your life?

_____

_____

_____

_____

_____

_____

_____

_____

_____

_____

_____

_____

_____

_____

_____

_____

_____

_____

_____

_____

_____

_____

_____

Often anxiety may be view as a future-oriented situation in which the solution involves problem-solving and preparing for the future outcome that you created.

Day 24

Depression is another commonly reported emotion. The prompts today examine thought patterns and memories that may contribute to feelings of depression. Anxiety is a future-orientated condition, while depression is associated with the past. At times depression can seem like an individual is walking through a museum of their history.

What items are currently on display in your emotional museum?

_____
_____
_____
_____
_____
_____
_____
_____
_____
_____
_____
_____
_____
_____
_____
_____
_____
_____
_____
_____
_____
_____
_____

DAY 24
Of the items on display in your emotional museum, which ones are things that you can change?

_____
_____
_____
_____
_____
_____
_____
_____
_____
_____
_____
_____
_____
_____
_____
_____
_____
_____
_____
_____
_____
_____
_____
_____
_____

DAY 24
What are the things you cannot change?

DAY 25

List an emotion that you frequently experience and describe how that emotion shows up in your body?

_____
_____
_____
_____
_____
_____
_____
_____
_____
_____
_____
_____
_____
_____
_____
_____
_____
_____
_____
_____
_____
_____
_____
_____
_____
_____
_____

DAY 25
If the emotion could speak, what would it say to you?

DAY 25
What problem is there to solve as a result of this emotion?

DAY 26
What brings joy to your life?

_____

_____

_____

_____

_____

_____

_____

_____

_____

_____

_____

_____

_____

_____

_____

_____

_____

_____

_____

_____

_____

_____

_____

_____

DAY 26
What are things that bring you a sense of calm and connection?

DAY 26

Thinking of the things that bring joy, calm, and connection to your life, create a chart to remind yourself to engage in these activities, and when possible, who can share these events with you.

You may use the chart below as an example. Utilize this chart to create a daily or weekly schedule of activities you can engage in when you want to experience joy. Allow this chart to remind you of the joy in your life. The activities in this chart will also become tools in your stress management toolbox.

Activities for Joy, Calm, and Connection			
Feeling	Activity /Situation	With whom	How often to engage in activity
Joy	Attend a movie	Xavier	1x a Week
Calm	Meditating	Alone	Daily
Connection	Meetings on Zoom	International Group	Monthly

Activities for Joy, Calm, and Connection			
Feeling	Activity /Situation	With whom	How often to engage in activity

© 2020

DAY 27

Awareness is the first step toward change; over the past several days, you have had an opportunity to become aware of emotions, body sensations, thoughts, and behaviors. Awareness, combined with action, creates change. Emotions may seem to appear without warning; often, the body will send signals before emotions and feelings escalate. The chart below can help you identify the range of your feelings and when you may take steps to prevent feelings from escalating. You can utilize the chart to decrease intensity if feelings have quickly approached five. The following chart is an example; your responses may vary.

FEELINGS AND EMOTION SCALE			
FEELING	**ANXIETY SCALE**		
INTENSITY	**REACTIONS**	**THOUGHTS**	**COPING/DE-ESCALATION STRATEGIES**
5	My body is shaking (or my body can't move), I'm crying. Beginning to feel very afraid.	My thoughts seem like they can't be controlled. "I can't get out of this situation."	Sit down and cry for a few minutes, wrap myself in a blanket, hug myself, call out for help, take medication, take full deep breaths, engage my senses in an activity to ground myself (ex. smell a scent, pinch myself, drink water)
4	My heart is beating very fast, speech is rapid, breathing is very shallow.	Difficulty concentration, "I can't think straight," "Oh no, something awful is happening".	Ask someone for help. Shake my body to burn off the energy. Leave the situation.
3	I'm in a room, and a lot of people begin to enter. My heartbeat starts to race more, and my breath becomes shallow.	This is too much, something wrong is going to happen. I'm going to have a panic attack.	Find a focus point (3) to quiet and calm thoughts. Rub my "worry stone," take log deep breaths, visualize myself in a calm place, tell someone I'm beginning to feel anxious. If possible, leave the room for a few minutes and get fresh air. Tell myself, "I'm okay," Look for an exit, look for something that creates a sense of safety.
2	Notice I'm going to be late for an event. Feeling a little rushed	I won't be able to make it, and I'll miss out, people will be upset with me.	Take a deep breath. Prioritize what needs to be done at the moment. Notify the other person I may be late.
1	Feeling calm, breathing is relaxed and at ease	Peaceful thoughts/thinking about the task to do	Maintain steady, easy breaths, review schedule for the day.
0	Very relaxed/sleeping comfortably	Minimal thoughts, if any they are peaceful dreams	Maintain sleep/stay relaxed

FEELINGS AND EMOTIONS SCALE

Utilize the following chart to identify an emotion that you would like to manage.

Step 1. Identify the emotion

Step 2. On the scale, record what the range of emotion looks like for you (0=low, 5=high).

Step 3. Identify a number where you would feel comfortable.

Step. 4. Identify actions to decrease escalation up the scale and maintenance at your comfort level.

FEELINGS AND EMOTION SCALE			
FEELING INTENSITY	*REACTIONS*	*THOUGHTS*	*COPING/DE-ESCALATION STRATEGIES*

DAY 28

Spend additional time in reflection today. Record the summary of your thoughts on this week.

_____

_____

_____

_____

_____

_____

_____

_____

_____

_____

_____

_____

_____

_____

_____

_____

_____

_____

_____

_____

_____

_____

_____

_____

_____

_____

WHITE TEA

White tea goes through minimal processing, and the leaves are not rolled or oxidized. White tea has little caffeine, approximately 18 mg, and is best with water boiled at 165°F/74°C and steeped for 2-3 minutes for loose leaf and 30-60 seconds for tea bags. White tea contains a high source of antioxidants, hydrates the body, promotes healthy skin, and relieves stress. If you like a smooth tea that's easy to drink without adding flavors or sweeteners, try white tea.

"Tea's proper use is to amuse the idle, and relax the studious, and dilute the full meals of those who cannot use exercise, and will not use abstinence" _
Essay on Tea 1757

YOUR BODY

This week, you will experience a slight shift from focusing on the mind to focus on the body. You will continue with self-exploration to help change thoughts and look at the physical aspects of self-care.

DAY 29
Where are your areas of tension and discomfort in your body?

_____

_____

_____

_____

_____

_____

_____

_____

_____

_____

_____

_____

_____

_____

_____

_____

_____

_____

_____

_____

_____

_____

_____

_____

_____

DAY 29
What does your body need to do when feeling tension and discomfort?

DAY 29

If the tension, discomfort, and aches in your body could talk, what would they say?

_____

_____

_____

_____

_____

_____

_____

_____

_____

_____

_____

_____

_____

_____

_____

_____

_____

_____

_____

_____

_____

_____

_____

_____

_____

DAY 30
What is your plan for reducing physical discomfort?

DAY 30
What do you need to do to accept any physical limits within your body?

_____

_____

_____

_____

_____

_____

_____

_____

_____

_____

_____

_____

_____

_____

_____

_____

_____

_____

_____

_____

_____

_____

_____

_____

_____

DAY 30
What is your plan for starting/maintaining physical activity?

_____

_____

_____

_____

_____

_____

_____

_____

_____

_____

_____

_____

_____

_____

_____

_____

_____

_____

_____

_____

_____

_____

_____

_____

_____

_____

DAY 31
As you think about your younger years or life as a child, what did you do for pleasure/fun?

DAY 31
Which of these activities are you continuing to do today?

DAY 31

What activities were you unable to do when younger, and how can you engage in these activities now?

_____
_____
_____
_____
_____
_____
_____
_____
_____
_____
_____
_____
_____
_____
_____
_____
_____
_____
_____
_____
_____
_____
_____
_____
_____

DAY 31
Which of these activities are you continuing to do today?

_____

_____

_____

_____

_____

_____

_____

_____

_____

_____

_____

_____

_____

_____

_____

_____

_____

_____

_____

_____

_____

_____

_____

DAY 31

What activities were you unable to do when younger, and how can you engage in these activities now?

_____
_____
_____
_____
_____
_____
_____
_____
_____
_____
_____
_____
_____
_____
_____
_____
_____
_____
_____
_____
_____
_____
_____
_____

DAY 32

Doing nothing is doing something. Sleep is vital to physical and mental well-being. An adult should average 7-9 hours of sleep per day.

What is your quality of sleep? How many hours of sleep per day?

_____
_____
_____
_____
_____
_____
_____
_____
_____
_____
_____
_____
_____
_____
_____
_____
_____
_____
_____
_____
_____
_____

DAY 32
What are you doing during the day that may have an impact on your sleep?

_____

_____

_____

_____

_____

_____

_____

_____

_____

_____

_____

_____

_____

_____

_____

_____

_____

_____

_____

_____

_____

_____

_____

DAY 32
List your nighttime/sleep schedule/hygiene. What changes do you need to make?

_____

_____

_____

_____

_____

_____

_____

_____

_____

_____

_____

_____

_____

_____

_____

_____

_____

_____

_____

_____

_____

_____

_____

_____

_____

_____

_____

_____

DAY 33

Are you what you eat? What's eating you? Nutrition is also essential for the body and emotions. Eating balanced meals, nutritious snacks and consulting with a nutritionist can be beneficial for your well-being.

As you think of your typical week, what food products are you likely to consume?

_____

_____

_____

_____

_____

_____

_____

_____

_____

_____

_____

_____

_____

_____

_____

_____

_____

_____

_____

_____

_____

_____

_____

DAY 33
List possible reactions you may have noticed with your eating habits.

DAY 33
What changes can you make with food/eating habits to create the changes you want to see in your life?

DAY 34

Thoughts, behaviors, feelings, emotions, eating, sleeping, work, self-care, responsibilities. Sometimes life can seem like it's filled with so much responsibility and such little time. Planning and following a schedule can be beneficial to overall wellness. When you create a schedule, you have a realistic picture of how you spend your day and available time in your day. Complete a weekly schedule and determine the degree to which your life feels balanced and where you may need to implement changes, multi-task, or ask for help. When completing a schedule, be sure to include time for events important to you, travel time, eating, hygiene, sleep, work, chores, and time for play. Creating a schedule does not have to include scheduling every minute, and you may start by scheduling one day, one hour, whatever you need at this time. Give yourself permission for some flexibility in your schedule. Aim for consistency over regimentation.

WEEKLY SCHEDULE

Time	Monday	Tuesday	Wednesday	Thursday	Friday	Saturday	Sunday
5:30							Sleep
			Morning Meditation/Reflection Time			Reflection/Exercise	
6:30			Walk and feed dog				
			Breakfast and Coffee			Walk and feed dog	
7:30			Prepare for Work/Shower Dress				Breakfast
						Shower/Dressed for day	
8:30			Commute to work				
						Biweekly Grocery	
9:30							Commute
							Spiritual Community
10:30						Clean House	
11:30							
			Work				
12:30						Visit	
						Family	
1:30						And	
						Friends	
2:30							
3:30							
							Meal Prep
4:30							
			Commute home				
5:30			Walk and feed Dog				
	Change clothes/unwind and Dinner				Change Clothes		
6:30							
	Yoga Class	Spin Class	Yoga Class	Cardio	Friends night out		
7:30							
			Commute home				
8:30			Evening Shower				
			Reading/Reflection time				
9:30			Nighttime ritual/Unwind				
					Home to unwind		
							Sleep
10:30			Sleep				
					Sleep		
11:30							

Record the time in half-hour increments. Your weekday can start with Monday and end with Saturday and Sunday. Start the schedule with things that you do on a daily and weekly basis. Include EVERYTHING, including waking and sleeping, travel time, meals, and any prep-time. If needed, make additional copies of the schedule to include any activities you may do on a biweekly or monthly basis. The time that you wake should be the same and should not vary much on the weekend.

WEEKLY SCHEDULE

	WEEKLY SCHEDULE						
	DAYS OF THE WEEK						
Time							

Record the time in half-hour increments. Your weekday can start with Monday and end with Saturday and Sunday. Start the schedule with things that you do on a daily and weekly basis. Include EVERYTHING, including waking and sleeping, travel time, meals, and any prep-time. If needed, make additional copies of the schedule to include any activities you may do on a biweekly or monthly basis. The time that you wake should be the same and should not vary much on the weekend.

DAY 35

Thinking back to day one, what changes have you noticed?

_____

_____

_____

_____

_____

_____

_____

What changes have you made in your life?

_____

_____

_____

_____

_____

_____

_____

What is your plan for continuing with these changes?

_____

_____

_____

_____

_____

_____

_____

HERBAL TEA

Herbal tea is a tea made of dried fruits, flowers, spices, and herbs, instead of Camellia Sinensis buds; it is not an official tea. Herbal teas are often caffeine-free and great thirst quenchers. Best served with water boiled at 208°F/98°C and steeped for 4-5 minutes for loose leaf and tea bags. Examples of Herbal teas are Rooibos and Hibiscus. These teas help with detoxifying the body and balancing potassium and sodium levels. Turmeric tea helps decrease swelling and rejuvenates muscles.

"Come and share a pot of tea, my home is warm and my friendship's free"
–Aniruddha Sastikar

COMMUNITY

An exploration of community is essential when examining well-being and mental health. The community can be a place of healing and, unfortunately, a place of hurt. This week examines the impact of community and sense of community belonging on mental health. A significant part of Alfred Adler's work explores the relationship between a person and their surroundings. Adler also believed a strong sense of community connection and giving back to the community (social interest and Gemeinschaftsgefuehl) was an indicator of well-being. Individuals cannot exist independently of their community. Existence occurs in the environment, and as such, it's essential to examine the relationship you have with your environment.

Community is not limited to your home environment and your neighborhood. Urie Bronfenbrenner's Ecological system describes five systems that represent the community: 1. Microsystem: Immediate family and household, 2. Mesosystem: Kinship and informal networks such as neighbors and cultural groups. 3.Exosystem: The local environment, formal networks, social services, mass media, governmental systems, health services, 4. Macrosystem: Broader economic, policy, social and broader environment, social norms and attitudes, climate, global economy. 5. Chronosystem: Changes that occur during a person's lifetime.

DAY 36
List and describe the communities that are part of your life.

_____

_____

_____

_____

_____

_____

_____

_____

_____

_____

_____

_____

_____

_____

_____

_____

_____

_____

_____

_____

_____

_____

_____

_____

DAY 36
What is your degree of connectedness to these communities?

_____

_____

_____

_____

_____

_____

_____

_____

_____

_____

_____

_____

_____

_____

_____

_____

_____

_____

_____

_____

_____

_____

_____

DAY 36
How does your sense of community impact your emotional/mental well-being?

DAY 37
In what ways do you feel connected (or disconnected) to your family?

_____

_____

_____

_____

_____

_____

_____

_____

_____

_____

_____

_____

_____

_____

_____

_____

_____

_____

_____

_____

_____

_____

_____

_____

DAY 37
Compare and contrast the adult role in your family with the role you had in your family as a child.

_____
_____
_____
_____
_____
_____
_____
_____
_____
_____
_____
_____
_____
_____
_____
_____
_____
_____
_____
_____
_____
_____
_____
_____
_____
_____

DAY 37
What changes would you like to see regarding your connection and role in your family?

_____
_____
_____
_____
_____
_____
_____
_____
_____
_____
_____
_____
_____
_____
_____
_____
_____
_____
_____
_____
_____
_____
_____
_____
_____
_____

DAY 38
Describe your current friendship circle. Is your friendship circle small/medium/large?

_____
_____
_____
_____
_____
_____
_____
_____
_____
_____
_____
_____
_____
_____
_____
_____
_____
_____
_____
_____
_____
_____
_____
_____
_____

DAY 38
How connected do you feel in your relationships with others?

_____

_____

_____

_____

_____

_____

_____

_____

_____

_____

_____

_____

_____

_____

_____

_____

_____

_____

_____

_____

_____

_____

_____

DAY 38

To what degree do you feel your contributions are valued, and you matter in relationships with others?

_____

_____

_____

_____

_____

_____

_____

_____

_____

_____

_____

_____

_____

_____

_____

_____

_____

_____

_____

_____

_____

_____

_____

_____

DAY 39
How would you define your religious/spiritual practice?

_____

_____

_____

_____

_____

_____

_____

_____

_____

_____

_____

_____

_____

_____

_____

_____

_____

_____

_____

_____

_____

_____

_____

_____

DAY 39
Record any changes in beliefs regarding your childhood/religion/spirituality with your adult views.

_____
_____
_____
_____
_____
_____
_____
_____
_____
_____
_____
_____
_____
_____
_____
_____
_____
_____
_____
_____
_____
_____
_____
_____
_____
_____

DAY 39
What aspects of your religious/spiritual practice are most sustaining for you?

DAY 40

In what way does your current household obligations/volunteer experiences/occupation/ add fulfillment to your life?

_____
_____
_____
_____
_____
_____
_____
_____
_____
_____
_____
_____
_____
_____
_____
_____
_____
_____
_____
_____
_____
_____
_____
_____

DAY 40
How does your current household obligations/volunteer experiences/occupation fulfill your life purpose?

DAY 40
What needs to change for your livelihood to be more meaningful and fulfilling?

DAY 41

This week you reflected on several parts of the community. As mentioned earlier this week, your relationship with the community plays a significant role in your well-being. The following chart combines four key elements that add to a sense of community connection and well-being. Think of your various levels of community when completing the following chart. Where and how can improvements be made?

Component of well-being	How and where is this experienced in your community	What actions can you take to improve upon these experiences/feelings
Feeling Connected "I have a sense of belonging and safety."	With family, at work, with my significant other.	I'd like to spend more time with my family. I'd like to interact with my coworkers outside of work.
Feeling Capable "I'm competent and have self-control."	I feel capable in my job. I want to feel more capable of keeping up the outward appearance of my home.	I could use my resources and get assistance with yard work to improve my home. I could learn how to do my repairs
Feeling that you matter "I make valuable contributions, and I matter."	My family reminds me that I matter. I'm not sure if I matter to my neighbors.	I can also become involved in the neighborhood association. Interact and get to know my neighbors.
Feeling Courageous "I feel hopeful, resilient, and can handle challenges."	My coworkers encourage me to ask for promotions.	Getting to know my neighbors and letting them know when I'm going out for a run helps me feel safer and resilient.

COMPONENTS OF WELL-BEING

Component of well-being	How and where is this experienced in your community	What actions can you take to improve upon these experiences/feelings
Feeling Connected "I have a sense of belonging and safety."		
Feeling Capable "I'm competent and have self-control."		
Feeling that you matter "I make valuable contributions, and I matter."		
Feeling Courageous "I feel hopeful, resilient, and can handle challenges."		

© 2020

DAY 42

Record your reflections on your community. In what ways did your view of community shift or expand over the past week?

_____

_____

_____

_____

_____

_____

_____

_____

_____

_____

_____

_____

_____

_____

_____

_____

_____

_____

_____

_____

_____

_____

TEA CEREMONY AND CELEBRATION

This week calls for a celebration. Tea ceremonies can be a way of beginning and ending significant events. A tea ceremony may include special tea ware, special teas, and your favorite treats. Allow yourself to savor the art of making and drinking tea this week.

CONGRATULATIONS!

You made it to the final week of this journal! How are you feeling? This week is devoted to the reflection of the previous weeks and bringing everything together. At the completion of this week, continue the process of journaling. If something came up while completing this journal, and you would like to deepen the exploration, consider contacting a professional to assist with the continuation of your journey.

DAY 43
What were the most significant insights discovered over the past weeks?

DAY 43
What strengths do you have that have helped with your resiliency and ongoing survival?

_____
_____
_____
_____
_____
_____
_____
_____
_____
_____
_____
_____
_____
_____
_____
_____
_____
_____
_____
_____
_____
_____
_____
_____

DAY 43
What's your next step as you keep moving forward?

DAY 44
What patterns did you notice in your life?

_____

_____

_____

_____

_____

_____

_____

_____

_____

_____

_____

_____

_____

_____

_____

_____

_____

_____

_____

_____

_____

_____

_____

_____

DAY 44
What is your understanding of the root cause of ongoing patterns in your life?

_____

_____

_____

_____

_____

_____

_____

_____

_____

_____

_____

_____

_____

_____

_____

_____

_____

_____

_____

_____

_____

_____

DAY 44

In what ways has this workbook helped you identify patterns in your life?

_____

_____

_____

_____

_____

_____

_____

_____

_____

_____

_____

_____

_____

_____

_____

_____

_____

_____

_____

_____

_____

_____

_____

_____

_____

DAY 45
What changes have you noticed within yourself over the past weeks?

DAY 45
What feelings/emotions come to mind when you think of these changes?

_____

_____

_____

_____

_____

_____

_____

_____

_____

_____

_____

_____

_____

_____

_____

_____

_____

_____

_____

_____

_____

_____

_____

_____

_____

_____

_____

DAY 45
In what ways are the changes beneficial in your life?

DAY 46
What did you find most rewarding as you worked through this workbook?

_____

_____

_____

_____

_____

_____

_____

_____

_____

_____

_____

_____

_____

_____

_____

_____

_____

_____

_____

_____

_____

_____

DAY 46
What was triggered or possible areas of discomfort as you worked through this book?

_____

_____

_____

_____

_____

_____

_____

_____

_____

_____

_____

_____

_____

_____

_____

_____

_____

_____

_____

_____

_____

_____

_____

_____

_____

DAY 46
How can you utilize the joys/discomforts to help in your life as you move forward?

_____

_____

_____

_____

_____

_____

_____

_____

_____

_____

_____

_____

_____

_____

_____

_____

_____

_____

_____

_____

_____

DAY 47
What current thoughts do you have regarding your past?

_____

_____

_____

_____

_____

_____

_____

_____

_____

_____

_____

_____

_____

_____

_____

_____

_____

_____

_____

_____

_____

DAY 47
What are your current thoughts regarding your relationships with others?

_____

_____

_____

_____

_____

_____

_____

_____

_____

_____

_____

_____

_____

_____

_____

_____

_____

_____

_____

_____

_____

_____

_____

DAY 47
What are your current thoughts regarding your relationship with yourself?

_____

_____

_____

_____

_____

_____

_____

_____

_____

_____

_____

_____

_____

_____

_____

_____

_____

_____

_____

_____

_____

_____

_____

DAY 48
In what ways were your intentions met?

_____
_____
_____
_____
_____
_____
_____
_____
_____
_____
_____
_____
_____
_____
_____
_____
_____
_____
_____
_____
_____
_____
_____
_____
_____
_____
_____

DAY 48
What changes occurred in your life over the past few weeks?

_____

_____

_____

_____

_____

_____

_____

_____

_____

_____

_____

_____

_____

_____

_____

_____

_____

_____

_____

_____

_____

_____

_____

_____

DAY 48
In what way did you accomplish what you wanted to achieve?

_____

_____

_____

_____

_____

_____

_____

_____

_____

_____

_____

_____

_____

_____

_____

_____

_____

_____

_____

_____

_____

_____

_____

DAY 49
What areas were not covered that need continued exploration?

DAY 49

What is the one thing that you will continue to do to help you move forward in improving and maintaining your mental health?

_____

_____

_____

_____

_____

_____

_____

_____

_____

_____

_____

_____

_____

_____

_____

_____

_____

_____

_____

_____

_____

_____

_____

DAY 49
What's next after the completion of these 49 days?

_____

_____

_____

_____

_____

_____

_____

_____

_____

_____

_____

_____

_____

_____

_____

_____

_____

_____

_____

_____

_____

_____

_____

_____

REFERENCES

Gibson E.L., Rycroft J.A. (2011) Psychological and Physiological Consequences of Drinking Tea. In: Preedy V., Watson R., Martin C. (eds) Handbook of Behavior, Food, and Nutrition. Springer, New York, NY. https://doi.org/10.1007/978-0-387-92271-3_41

Hart, William (1987), The Art of Living: Vipassana Meditation As Taught by S.N. Goenka HarperCollins

Resource for Tea: https://www.republicoftea.com/

PDF link for charts contained in this book: https://teaandtherapy.info/Worksheets

Made in the USA
Monee, IL
06 February 2021